Cells, Tissues & Organ Systems: Glossary

 **Minerals:** elements or compounds, found in nature as rocks.

 **Muscle Tissue:** made up from cells that can shorten.

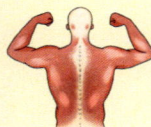 **Muscular:** made up from muscle tissue.

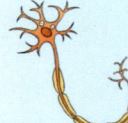 **Nerve Tissue:** made up from nerve cells.

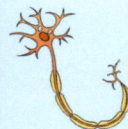 **Neuron:** a nerve cell.

 **Nutrients:** the products of digested food.

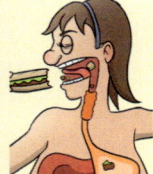 **Oesophagus (ee-sof-a-gus):** the tube that connects the mouth to the stomach.

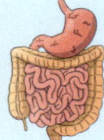 **Organ:** made up from different types of tissue and has an important function.

 **Plasma:** the straw coloured liquid that forms most of the blood. It is mainly water.

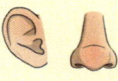 **Receptors:** the eyes, skin, tongue, nose and ears.

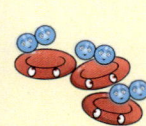 **Red Blood Cells:** a biconcave cell that carries oxygen to all cells of the body. No nucleus.

 **Sperm Cells:** The male sex cell.

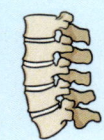 **Spinal Cord:** The nerve tissue that runs through the middle of the spine. Part of the CNS.

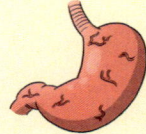 **Stomach:** a small muscular bag. Part of the digestive system.

 **Tissue:** a group of identical cells working together.

 **Transport:** to move from one place to another.

 **Villi:** a finger-like projection from the small intestine wall. They make the surface area of the intestine much bigger.

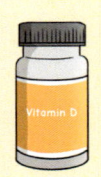 **Vitamins:** a group of chemical compounds, found in food, needed in small amounts for healthy growth and repair.

Animal Cells and Tissues

1 Cells, Tissues and Organs

- Our bodies are made up of **billions of cells**.

- **Different types** of cells carry out **different jobs**.

- **Red blood cells** carry **oxygen** all around the body.

- **Sperm cells** have a **tail** for swimming.

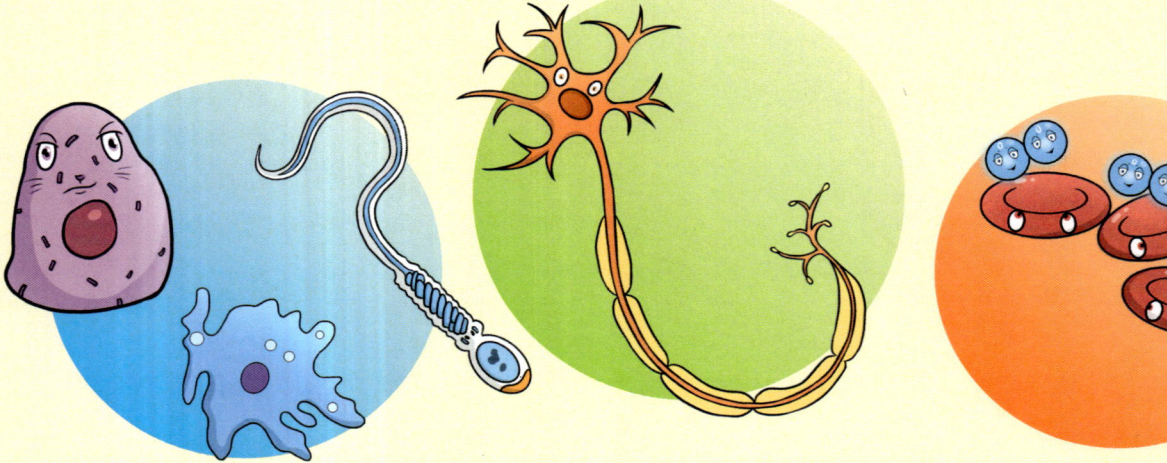

2 Tissues

- When a group of the **same type** of cell work together, we call it a **tissue**.

- Our bodies are made up of over **200 different types** of **tissue**.

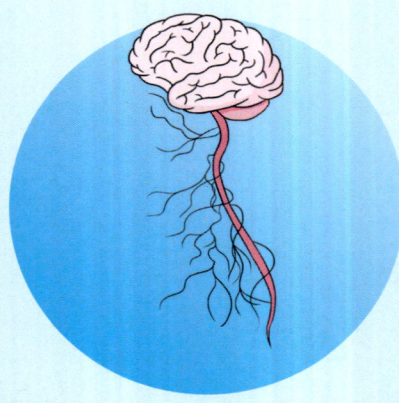

3 Tissues

- **Nerve tissue** carries **messages** to and from the **brain**.

- **Fatty tissue** (under our skin) helps to **insulate** our bodies.

Fatty Tissue

Organ Systems

 Animal Organs

- **Organs** are made up from different **types of tissue**.

- Each organ has a special job.

- Our **skin** is the **biggest organ** of the body.

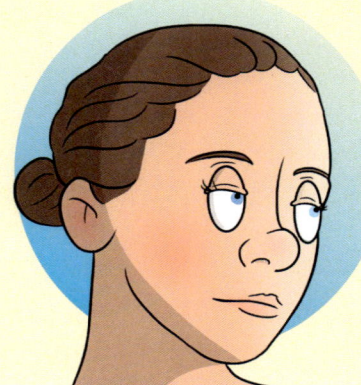

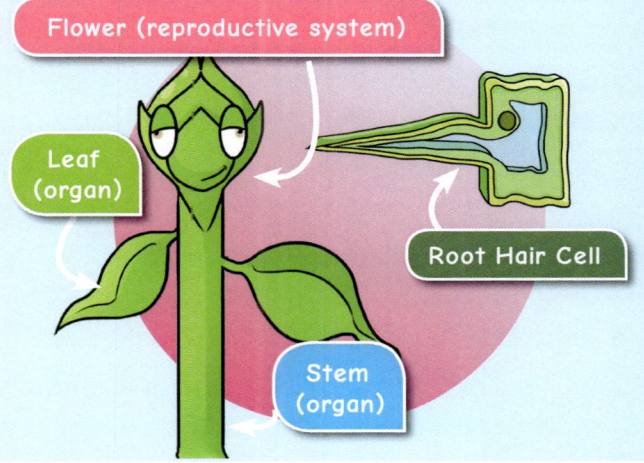 **Plant Organs**

- Plants also have **cells**, **tissues** and **organs**.

- There is more about this in our Plant Reproduction Topic Pack.

Flower (reproductive system)

Leaf (organ)

Root Hair Cell

Stem (organ)

 Organ Systems

- Different organs **work together**.

- Organs working together are called **organ systems**.

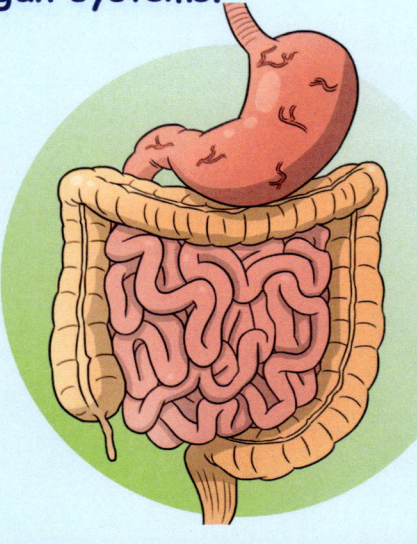

 Working Together

- In animals the **mouth**, **stomach** and **intestines** work together.

- They are the **digestive system**.

Organs of the Digestive System

8 The Digestive System

- The organs of the **digestive system** digest and **absorb** the food we eat.

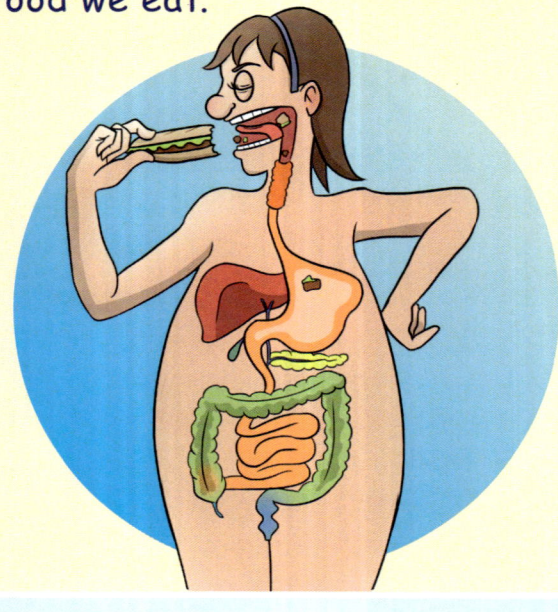

9 Different Jobs

- The **different organs** carry out **different jobs**.

10 Chewing Food

- The **mouth** starts the **breakdown** of food by **chewing** it.

11 Tongue

- The **tongue** has lots of muscle tissue.

- It moves the food to your **throat** to be **swallowed**.

Organs of the Digestive System

12 Stomach

- Food passes down a tube called the **oesophagus** (uh-sof-ay-gus) into your **stomach**.

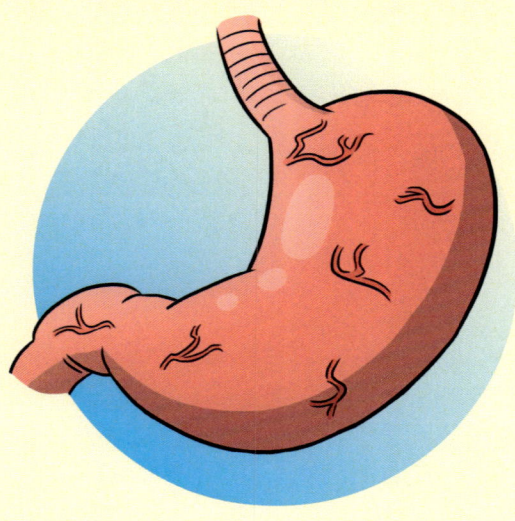

13 Muscle Tissue

- Your **stomach** is about the size of your **fist**.

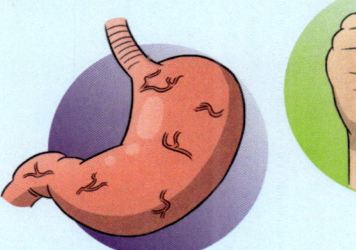

- The **stomach** looks like a small bag or a whoopee cushion!

- It has lots of **muscle** tissue.

14 Contracting Muscles

- The muscle tissue gently **contracts** and **relaxes**.

- **It mixes** the **food** and **enzymes**.

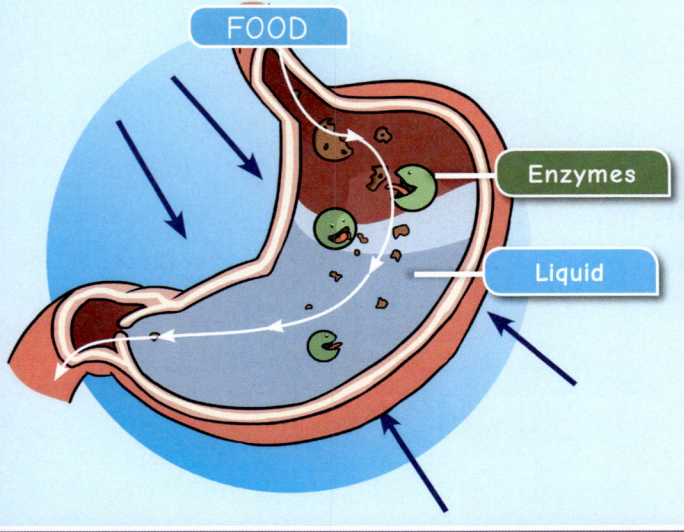

FOOD

Enzymes

Liquid

15 Small Intestine

- Food from the **stomach** is squeezed into the **small intestine**.

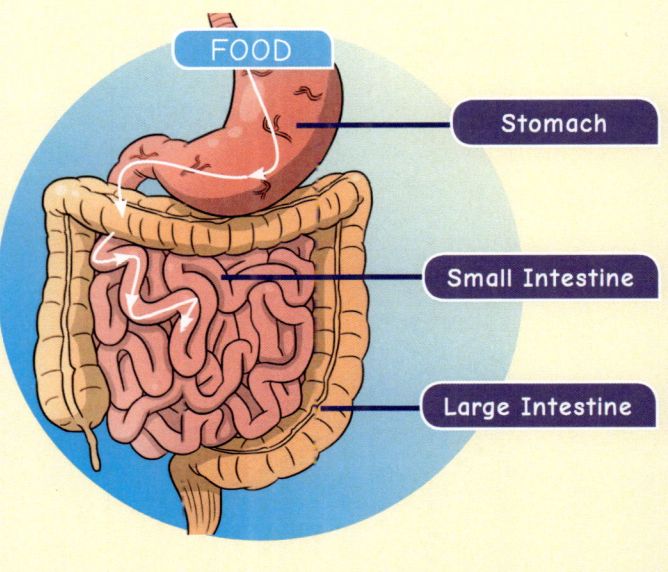

FOOD

Stomach

Small Intestine

Large Intestine

16 Small Intestine

- The **small intestine** is very long (about **7m** in an adult).

- It only has a **small diameter**.

- It has rings of muscle that **contract in waves**.

- This pushes the food along.

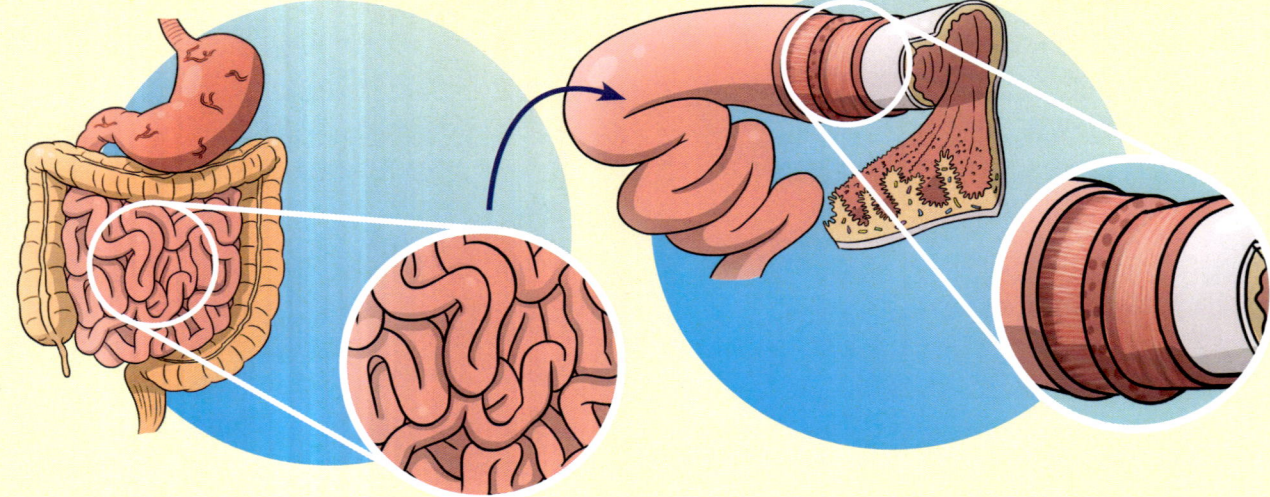

17 Increased Surface Area - An Adaptation

- The **surface** has lots of folds with **villi and microvilli**.

- This gives it a **large surface area** to **absorb** digested food.

- The **undigested food** is squeezed into the **large intestine**.

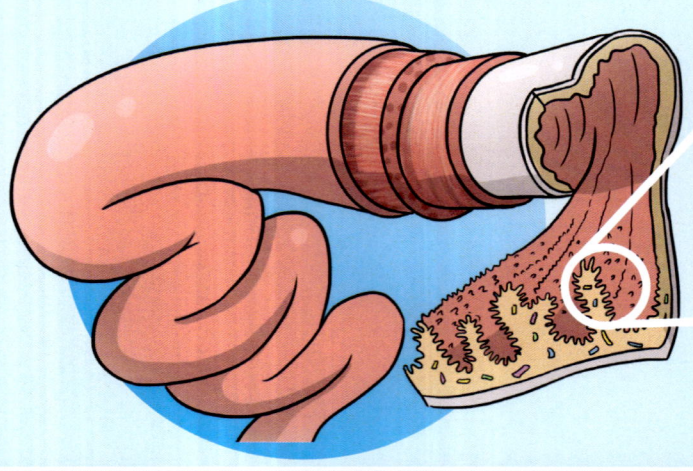
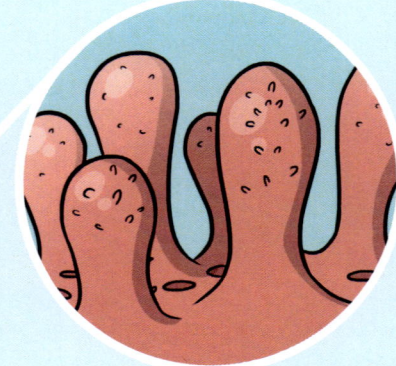

Organs of the Digestive System

18   Large Intestine

- The large intestine is quite **short** (about 1½m in an adult).

- It has a **large** diameter.

- The large intestine has **fewer folds**.

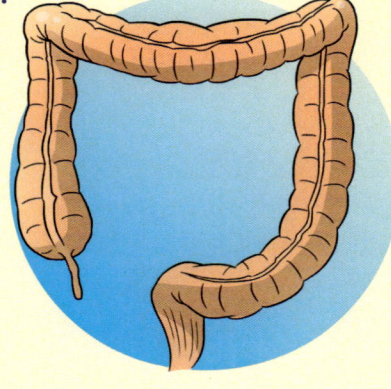

19   Absorption

- It **absorbs water, vitamins** and **minerals**.

Water

Vitamins & Minerals

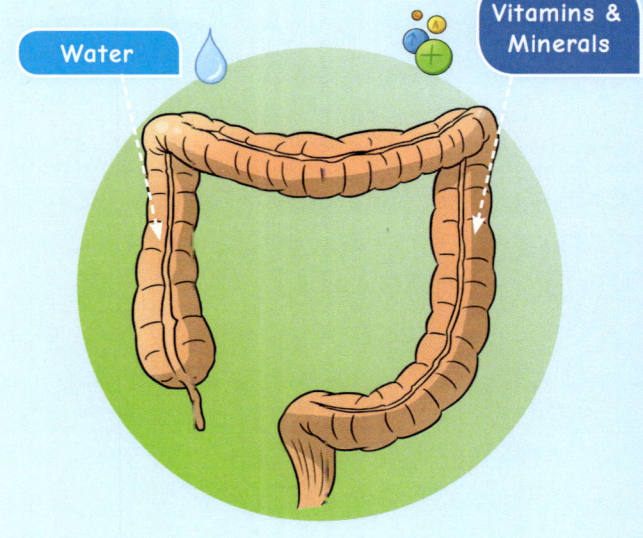

20   Bacteria

- **Bacteria** breaks down the **waste** food before it turns into **faeces**.

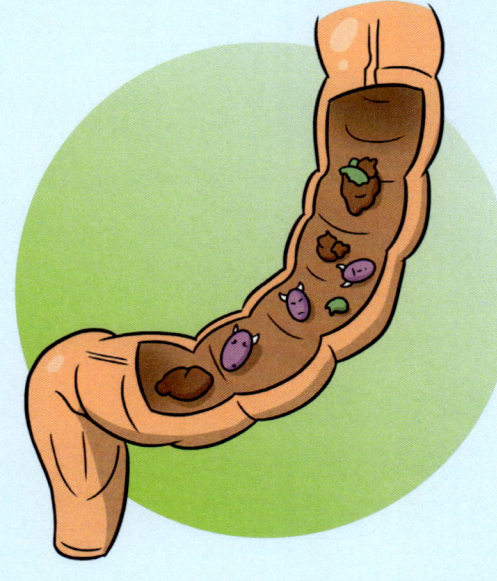

21   Undigested Food

- The **undigested food** then **leaves** the body during **egestion**.

- Faeces **leaves** the body through the **anus**.

Organs of the Circulatory System

22   Transport System

- The **circulatory system** is the **transport system** for our bodies.

- The **blood, heart and blood vessels** are **organs** of the **circulatory system**.

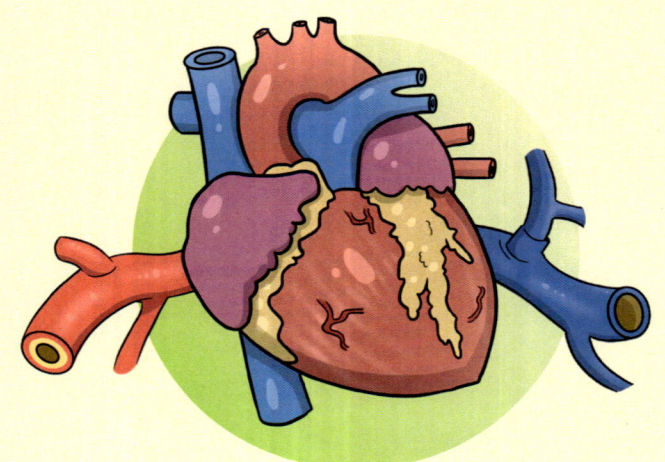
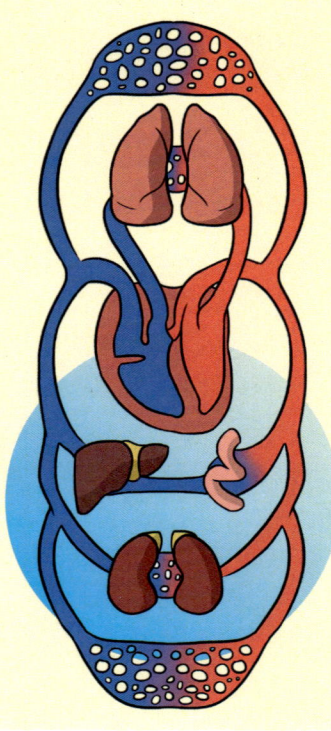

23   Transporting Nutrients and Oxygen

- It transports **digested food and oxygen** to all parts of the body.

- Our bodies have over **100,000km** of **blood vessels!**

- **Blood** is made up from cells that float in a **watery liquid** called **plasma.**

Plasma

Blood Vessel

Red Blood Cells

White Blood Cells

Platelets

Organs of the Circulatory System

24   Transportation

- **Nutrients and waste products** dissolve in the plasma for **transportation**.

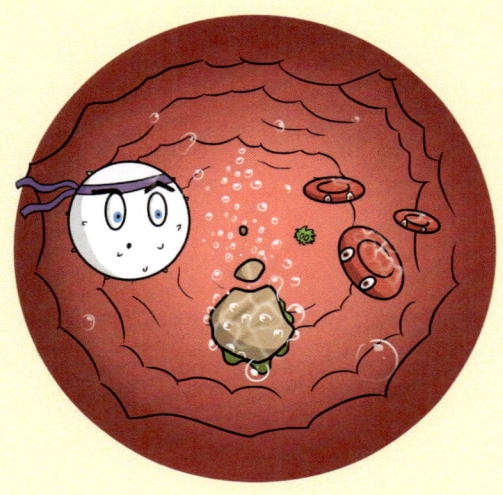

25   Important Cells

- **Blood** contains **white blood cells.**

- They help us **fight disease and infections.**

26   Cells With A Special Job!

- **Platelets** help the blood to **clot** when we have a cut.

Platelets clotting a blood vessel

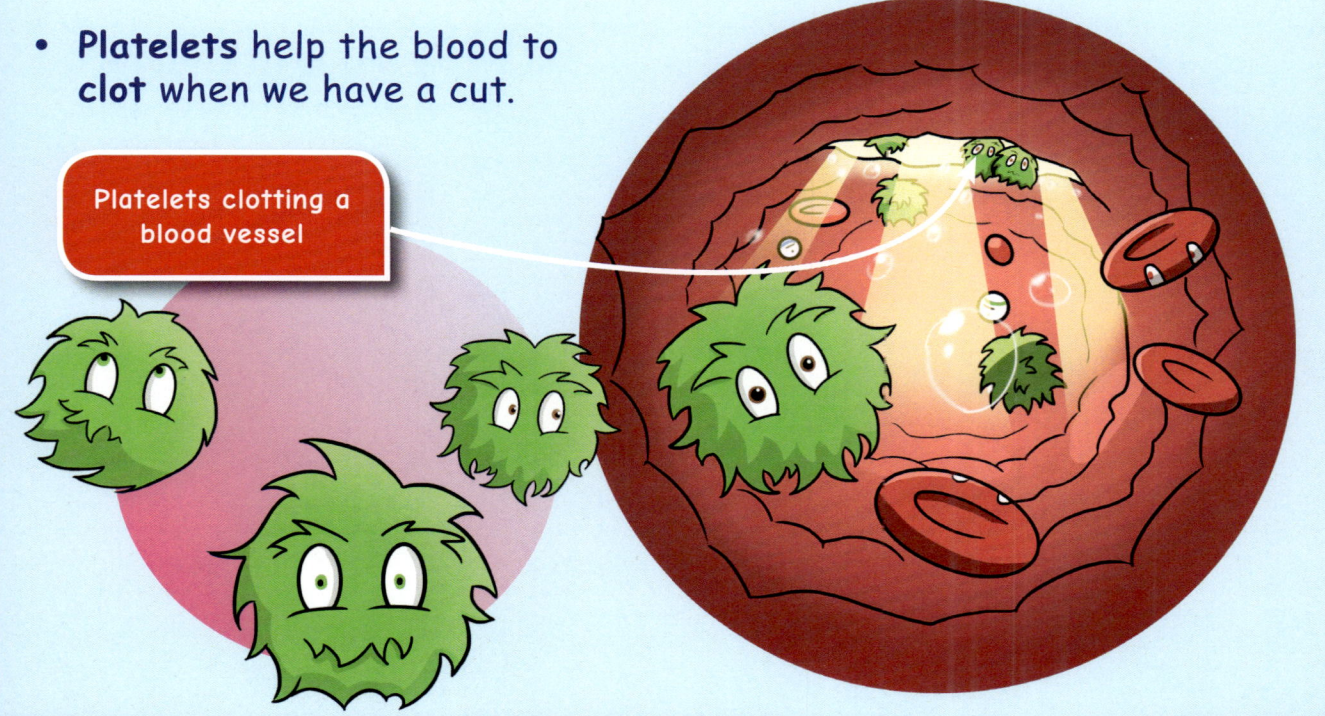

Organs of the Circulatory System

27 Red Blood Cells

- **Red blood cells** carry **oxygen from** the lungs **to** other **organs**.

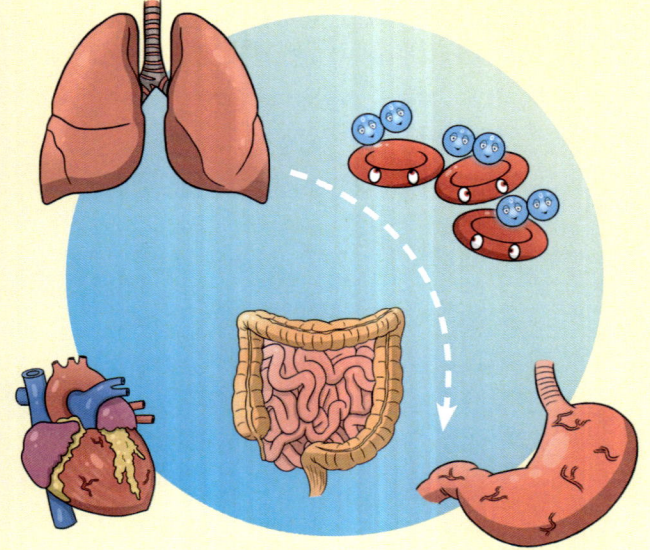

28 The Heart

- The **heart,** like the stomach, is about the size of a **fist**.

- It is a **pump** that beats about **60 times per minute**.

- It will do this for 80, 90 or even 100 years.

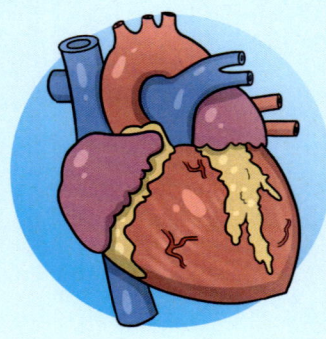

29 Cardiac Tissue

- The **heart** is made from a very **special** type of **tissue** called **cardiac** tissue.

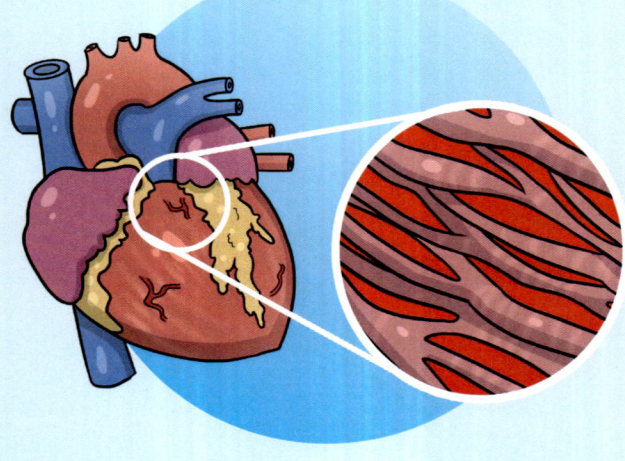

30 4 Chambers

- The heart has **four** chambers surrounded by **thick muscle**.

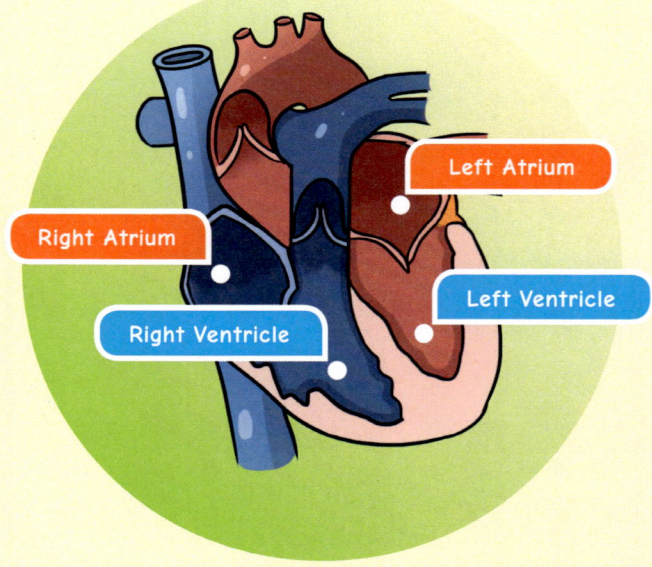

Left Atrium

Right Atrium

Left Ventricle

Right Ventricle

Organs of the Circulatory System

31   Blood from Lungs

- The **left atrium** collects **blood** from the **lungs**.

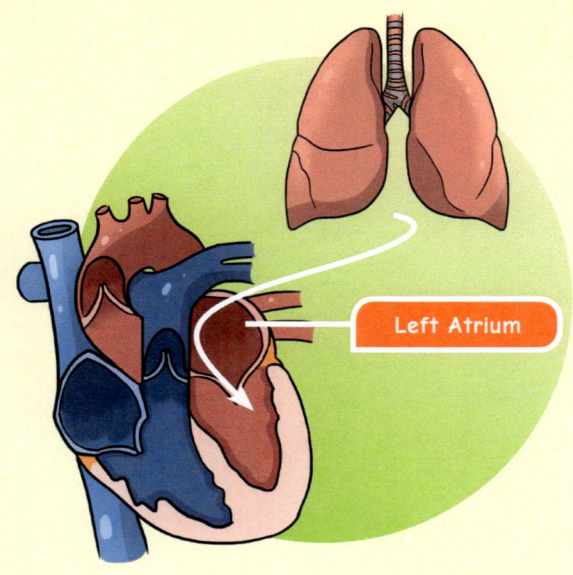

Left Atrium

32   Ventricles

- The **two bottom chambers** are pumping chambers.

- They are the **right ventricle and left ventricle**.

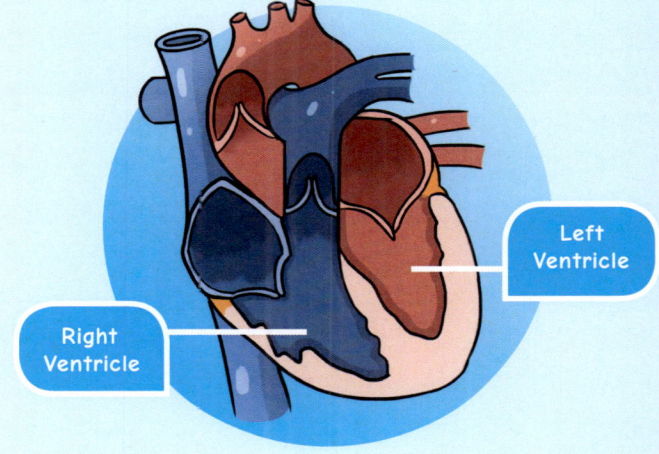

Left Ventricle

Right Ventricle

33   Blood to Lungs

- The **right ventricle** pumps blood **from** the body **to** the **lungs**.

- Blood collects **oxygen** in the **lungs**.

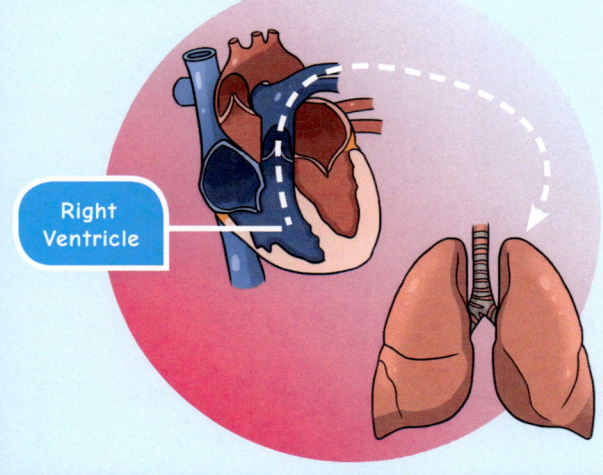

Right Ventricle

34   Oxygenated Blood
(ox-ee-jen-ay-ted)

- The **left ventricle** pumps blood full of oxygen to the **head** and **body**.

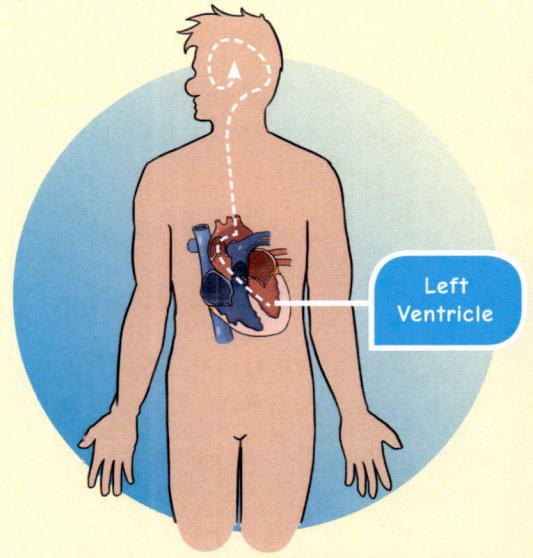

Left Ventricle

Organs of the Circulatory System

35   Heart Beat

- When the muscle of the heart **contracts** we call it a **heart beat**.

- The blood is forced **from the top chambers**, through the **valves**, into the **bottom chambers**.

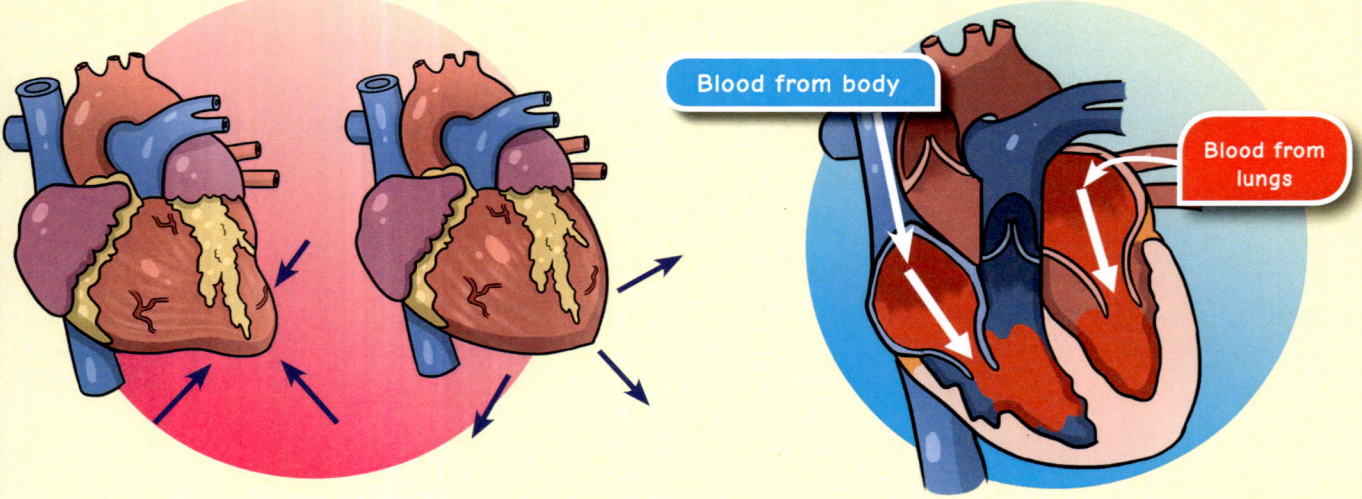

Blood from body

Blood from lungs

36   Contractions

- As heart **muscle** continues to contract, the **blood** is forced out from the **bottom chambers**.

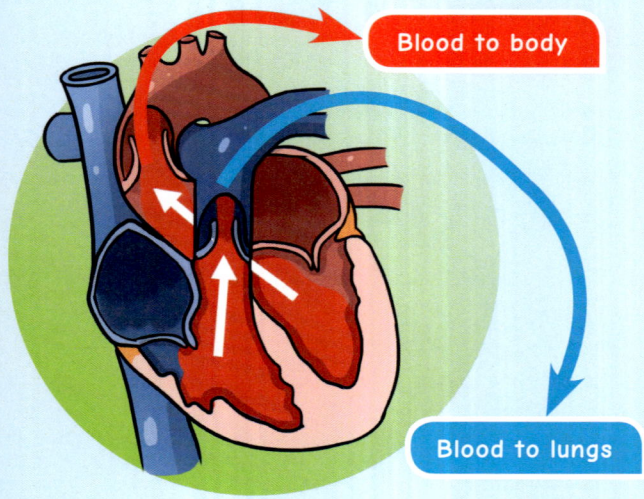

Blood to body

Blood to lungs

37   Double Circulatory (not tested for CE)

- Blood **travels** through the **heart twice**, during each **circulation** around the body.

- It is called a **double circulatory system**.

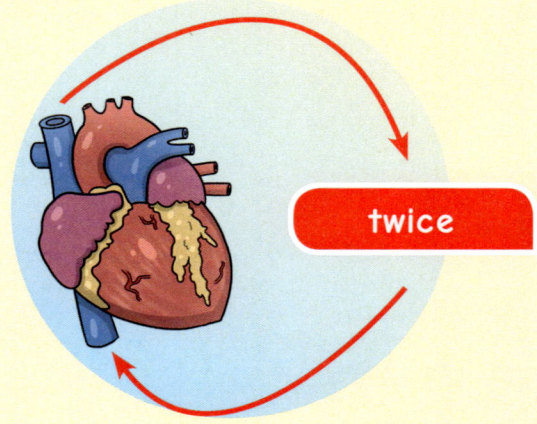

twice

Organs of the Circulatory System

38   Blood Vessels

- The circulatory system consists of the **heart pumping blood** through the **blood vessels** of the body.

- As the blood goes around the body, it goes through **three types** of blood vessels.

39   1. Arteries

- **Arteries** are tubes that have **thick walls** made from **muscle** and **elastic** tissue.

- **Arteries** carry blood at **high pressure** away from the heart. They are like motorways.

A= Away from heart

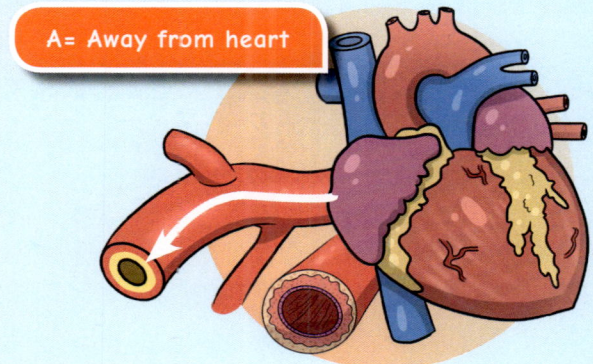

40   2. Veins

- **Veins** are tubes with **thin walls** made from muscle and elastic tissue.

- **Veins** carry low **pressure** blood **towards** the heart.

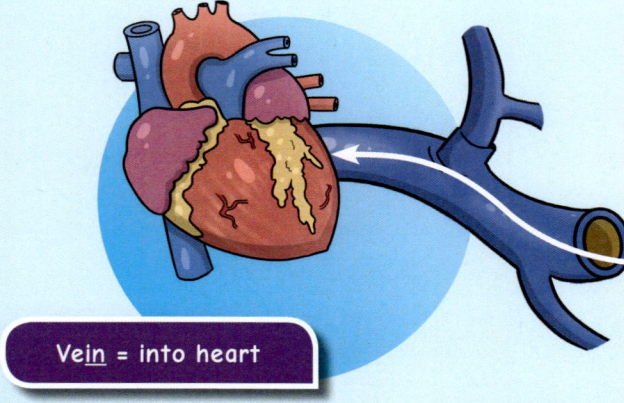

Vein = into heart

41   3. Capillaries

- Capillary walls are just one cell thick.

- Nutrients are **delivered** to cells and **waste** is **collected** through the **capillaries**.

- They are like narrow roads in the town where things go slowly and can drop stuff off.

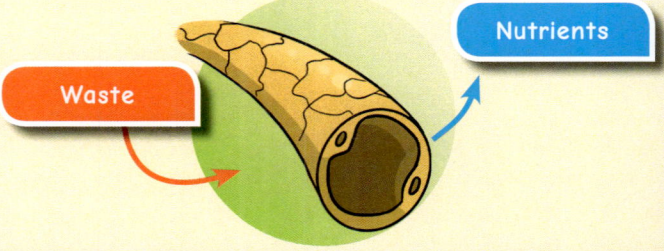

Waste

Nutrients

42 The Nervous System (not tested for CE)

- The nervous system is divided into 2 parts.

- CNS (Central Nervous System)

- Peripheral Nervous System

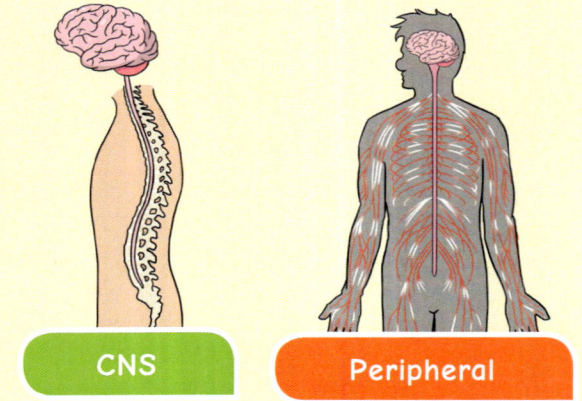

CNS   Peripheral

43 Central Nervous System

- The Central Nervous System (CNS) is made up of the **brain**, and **spinal cord.**

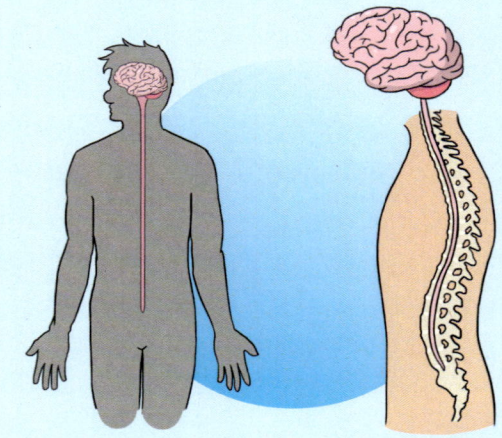

44 Nervous System

- The **spinal cord** carries **signals** from **receptors** to the **brain.**

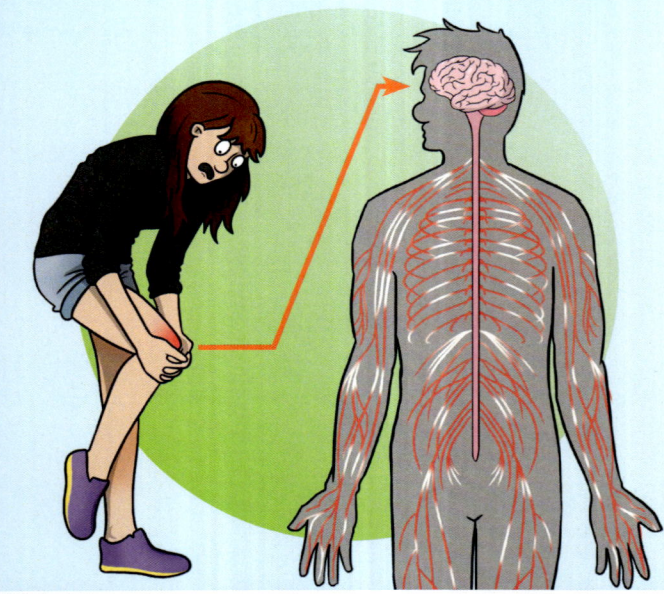

45 Peripheral (per-if-er-al) Nervous System

- The **peripheral nervous system** is made up from all other **nerves** (neurons) and **receptors.**

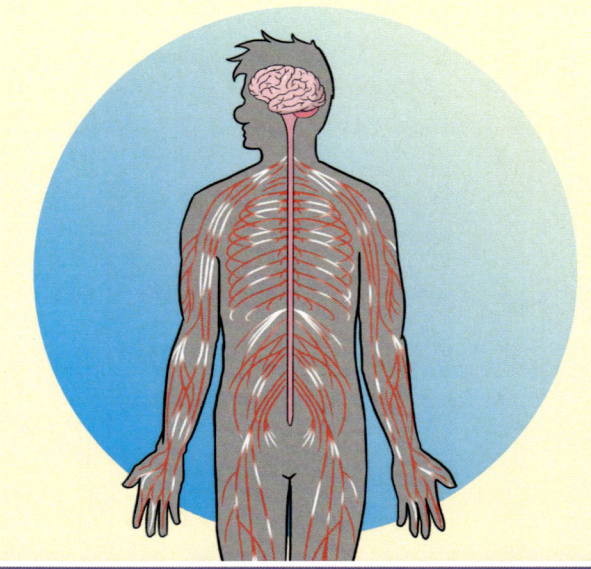

Organs of the Nervous System
(not tested for CE)

46 Spinal Cord

- The **peripheral nervous system** connects the **brain** through the **spinal cord**.

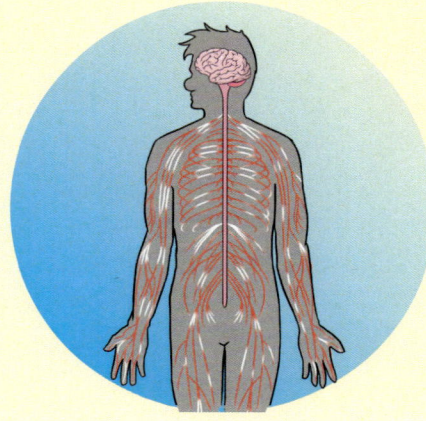

47 Neurons

- Neurons **connect** all parts of the nervous system **together**.

- **Neurons** carry **electrochemical signals**.

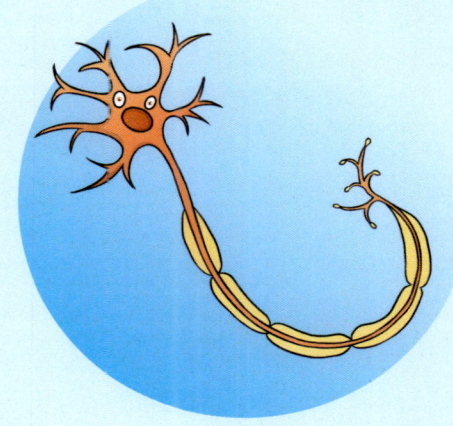

48 Longest Neuron!

- The **longest neuron** reaches from our big toe to our spine.

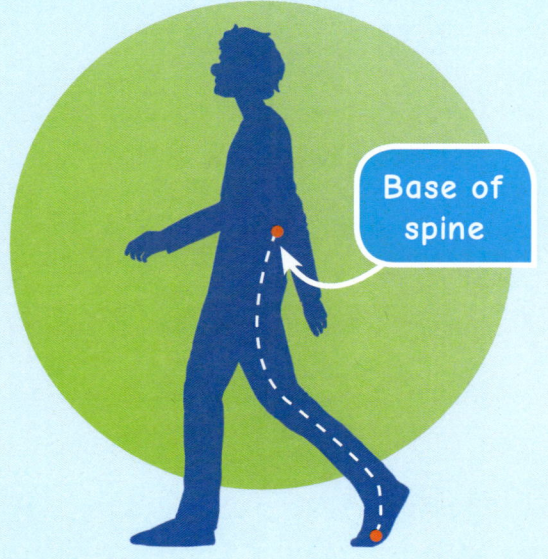

Base of spine

49 Sensory Neurons

- **Sensory neurons** carry signals from **receptors** to the **brain**.

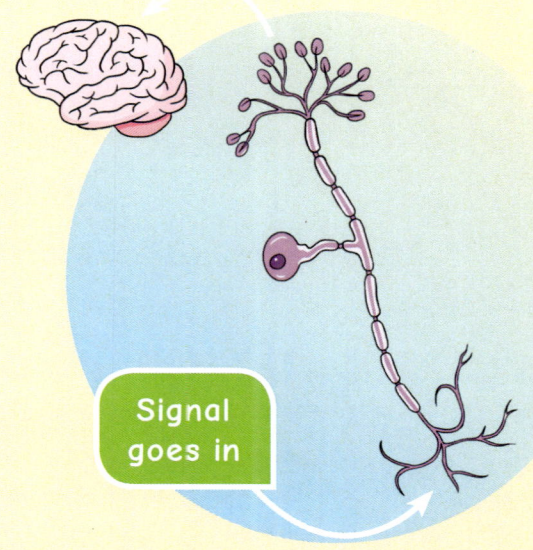

Signal goes in

Organs in a Plant

- Remember: plants are living organisms too!
- They are made up of different cells.
- As the plant grows, the cells develop to make plant tissues and organs.
- The organs let the plant perform life processes.

Flowers are organs needed for reproduction

- Colour and smell attracts insects for pollination.
- The flower makes the sex cells.
- When the petals fall, the flower becomes the fruit.
- The fruit contains the seeds.

The stem is an organ needed for reproduction and nutrition.

- It holds the flower up for insects and wind pollination.
- It holds the leaves up to the light for photosynthesis.
- It contains tubes that let water and nutrients move around the plant (transport system).

Roots are organs needed for nutrition and keep the plant in place.

- They hold the plant in the soil.
- They grow down to find water.
- They have root hair cells adapted to absorb water and nutrients from the soil.

Leaves are organs needed for nutrition.

- Chlorophyll traps sunlight for photosynthesis.
- They have a large surface area for photosynthesis.
- They have cells adapted to let gases diffuse in and out.